# THE DARTMOOR STANNARIES

Tin-Mining on Dartmoor in the Middle Ages
1100-1600

by **PAUL HAMBLING**

First Published 1995 by
Orchard Publications
2 Orchard Close, Chudleigh, Newton Abbot, Devon TQ13 0LR
Telephone: (01626) 852714

ISBN 1 898964 12 2

*Designed, Typeset and Printed by*
Swift Print
Dawlish
Devon EX7 9HP

# CONTENTS

# INTRODUCTION

Today most visitors to Dartmoor think of it first as a National Park, a picturesque wilderness full of what the Victorians called Wild Romantic Prospects. They may also be aware of it as a farming landscape, if only because of the obvious presence of cattle, sheep and ponies; but often they are surprised to learn that from the early Middle Ages to the start of the 20th century it was a centre of intensive industrial activity.

Scarcely a hillside or valley is without some evidence of the tin-miners who once laboured there. Often the whole character of the landscape is their handiwork, with its winding leats, heather-choked gullies and piles of debris hidden under grass and bracken. The 19th century played its part in this transformation, but the face of the moor had already been changed long before by the 'old men' of the Middle Ages, with their crude tools and hard-won skills. In the following pages we explain how they lived and worked, and how their world was organised.

The information contained here was first compiled for the 'Dartmoor Stannaries' exhibition which opened at the Museum of Dartmoor Life, Okehampton, in September 1994, one of a number of events held through-out Devon to celebrate the 500th anniversary of the 1494 Tinners' Parliament at Crockern Tor. Jo Hughes and Samantha Bowring assisted with research and wrote parts of the original text. Chief among those who gave help and advice was Alan Endacott MA, AMA, curator of the Museum of Dartmoor Life, who took the photographs for this book as well as doing most of the hard work of designing and mounting the exhibition. The author acknowledges a debt to many other writers, especially those listed in the bibliography.

P.H. 1995

# THE VALUE OF TIN

*The third comoditie [of Devon] also is the number of the mines in the countrie of which some do yelde gold, some sylver, some ledd, some copper and some iron: but the cheaffe is Tin.*

John Hooker, alias John Vowell, *Synopsis Chorographical of Devonshire*, c. 1598-99

**Why was tin valuable?**
Tin is a soft, easily-worked metal, which combines well with other metals to form alloys, such as pewter (tin and lead) and bronze (tin and copper). These were in great demand in the Middle Ages, when many people ate and drank from pewter utensils, and pewter jewellery and belt-ornaments were popular with the majority who could not afford precious metals such as silver. Bronze was used for bell-casting, and in the later Middle Ages for making cannon and other firearms.

In his *Survey of Cornwall* in 1602, Richard Carew wrote: '*Tin... is in working so pliant, for sight so fair, and in use so necessary, as thereby the inhabitants gain wealth, the merchants traffic, and the whole realm a reputation... In travelling abroad, in tarrying at home, in eating and drinking, in doing ought of pleasure or necessity, tin either in its own shape, or transformed into other fashions, is always requisite, always ready for our service.*

**Where was tin found?**
Tin-bearing rocks are found in only a few areas of Europe. The granite region of South West England is one such place, and in Devon the tin deposits are concentrated in the granite plateau forming the medieval Forest of Dartmoor.

Cornish tin was known and exported in ancient times, but there is no definite evidence of tin-working on Dartmoor before the Middle Ages. It has been argued that the early bronze-using inhabitants would not have failed to recognise signs of plentiful tin deposits, and that evidence of ancient tin-extraction has been obliterated by later workings. Traces of tin slag have in fact been found on one Bronze Age site, but they may have been introduced later, and the question of when Dartmoor tin was first exploited remains open.

Extensive tin-working had certainly begun within a hundred years of the Norman Conquest (1066). The first written evidence, in 1198, describes an industry already flourishing, with established customs and liberties. For about fifty years during the second half of the 12th century, when untapped alluvial deposits were being opened up, Dartmoor not only outstripped Cornwall, but became the largest producer of tin in Europe.

A commodity so valuable naturally became of great financial importance not only to the people of the Dartmoor area, but to the economy of the whole country. A 16th century account of the Devon tin industry, or stannary, makes this clear.

*The stannary hath contynued in workinge to the greate increase of the revenue of the said Erledome or Duchie and the meantenance of great nombres of house-holdes, families and inhabitantes bothe of the said countrie and of sundrie townes within this realme but especially of London and of the merchantes of the same who do not onely worke the same but do also transporte the same into other countries and nations than which there is not a better merchandyse ...*

John Hooker, alias John Vowell, *Synopsis Chorographical of Devonshire,* c. 1598 - 99.

3

# HOW THE TIN WAS MINED

*They may dig tyn & turves for melting of tyn everywhere in our lands moors and wastes & of all other persons whatsoever ... and the waters & water courses for the works of the Stannaryes to turn where & as often as need shall be & to buy bushement for the melting of tyn as of old tyme hath bin accustomed to be done ...*

*A true Copie of the Charter or grant*
*made by King Edward the first, 1305.*

### Extracting the ore

Dartmoor tin was found in the form of tinstone or cassiterite (oxide of tin). Rich deposits of this heavy black sand and gravel, washed down from the parent lodes by the action of water over millions of years, lay under the lighter material of the stream beds and valley floors, where it could be obtained by simple shovelling and panning. It was these easily-accessible deposits that fuelled the first great expansion of the industry, as the tinners worked their way along nearly every stream on the moor, casting up mounds of debris on the banks. The method was called streaming, and produced a distinctive landscape of parallel or concentric ridges and channels still to be seen all over Dartmoor today. Examples near Okehampton are at the head

*Concentric ridges - The stream-working at Ivy Tor Water on South Tawton Common shows the typical landscape of concentric ridges created by the early tinners. As each strip of the valley floor was turned over, channels of water were diverted through the workings to wash away the lighter debris from the heavy tin ore. The straight line visible behind is a prehistoric reeve, or boundary wall.*

of Ivy Tor Water (properly called Lettabrook or Ladybrook) on South Tawton Common (map reference SX 629917); at Taw Marsh on the River Taw above Belstone; and at Skit Bottoms (606910) on the upper East Okement.

Stream-working continued to the 17th century and even later; but once the richest valley-bottom deposits had been exhausted, more complex methods came into use. By careful observation of soil and vegetation, and digging small test pits into the rising ground of the valley slopes, it was possible to trace the course of the lodes from which the 'stream tin' had originally come. Ore could then be mined with pick and shovel from shallow trenches cut 'on the back of the lode'. Such gullies were called beamworks, and are normally aligned east to west, since this is the prevailing direction of tin lodes on Dartmoor.

Wherever possible, streams of water would be diverted through the workings, to help in washing away the lighter waste. This was done by building artificial channels or leats to carry the water, and sometimes reservoirs to collect it; such a pond can be seen in association with beamworks at Challacombe Down on Manaton Common (SX 691802). Everything was accomplished with only the simplest of tools. Wooden buckets and crude picks and shovels were all the early tinners needed to change the face of the Dartmoor landscape.

During the Middle Ages most Dartmoor tin-digging continued to be from open trenches or pits, partly because ore remained available near the surface, but also because of the water which rapidly accumulated in any excavation. In the 15th and 16th centuries some vertical shafts may have been sunk, but are unlikely to have gone below the level where they could be drained by tunnels, or adits, driven through the hillside to a nearby valley. Deep underground mining came to Dartmoor only in the 18th and 19th centuries, as new kinds of pumping and hoisting gear were introduced.

## Crushing and dressing

When a sufficient quantity of tinstone had been collected, it had to be crushed finely and rinsed to remove as much waste material as possible. The whole process was known as the 'wash', and normally took place twice a year, in May and September.

The rich alluvial ores of the early days were already reduced to small pebbles by water action, and needed little more than a final grinding in stone mortars. Ore dug from the lode included a greater proportion of worthless rock, and came in larger pieces that were much more difficult to crush by hand. Production fell drastically as the alluvial deposits were depleted, and began to recover only with the introduction of mechanical methods of ore-dressing in the 14th and 15th centuries.

The earliest of the new developments was the crazing mill, in which partly-crushed ore was ground to particles between circular millstones, much as in a flour mill. The stones were probably turned at first by men or horses, but later were water-powered. Crazing mills speeded the later stages of crushing, but gave no help in reducing large stones, and seem never to have been universally adopted.

More crucial was the invention of the knacking or knocking mill, which mechanised the pestle-and-motar method of crushing. It consisted of two or three heavy, iron-shod wooden posts called stamps, working up and down in a frame and pounding the ore beneath them. Powered by a small water-wheel, the stamps could hammer the largest chunks of ore to a fine gravel ready for the crazing mill. A further refinement came at the end of the 16th century, when it was found that if the ore was crushed while wet it could be reduced to powder by stamping alone. The crazing mill was no longer needed, and stamps of the same basic pattern remained in use down to the very end of the Dartmoor tin industry, about 1930.

The last stage of dressing involved placing the fine-crushed ore in shallow pits or troughs called buddles, where it was stirred in flowing water to wash away the lighter waste. The concentrate that remained was known as black tin, and in this form would be weighed and shared between the partners in the mining venture. Black tin was often

*Buddles - The crushed ore was stirred in shallow troughs of flowing water to wash away the lighter waste.*

bought and sold, but to prevent tax-evasion the sale had to be made openly at the wash, or before witnesses. Only recognised tinners were supposed to possess unsmelted tin, and it was not allowed to be taken out of the county.

## Smelting

To convert the black tin into metallic white tin required heating, or smelting. In the earliest times this would be done simply by buidling a peat fire over the heaped ore at the mine site, and raking up tin from the ashes. The metal produced by such low-temperature smelting would be gritty and impure, and needed smelting a second time to bring it to the required standard. This had to be done at a designated place, in the presence of a royal official who would weigh the metal and check its purity, stamp it with the royal mark, and collect the taxes imposed by the crown. The *Furnum Regis,* or King's Oven, near Postbridge may have been one such smelting-place, but more usually the process was carried out at a market town, where buyers would gather to bid for the tin.

In 1305 the towns of Tavistock, Ashburton and Chagford were appointed permanent centres for taxing and marketing Dartmoor tin. Plympton was added to the group in 1328, and these became the four Stannary Towns of Devon. Each controlled a district also called a stannary.

During the 13th century smelting gradually became more efficient, as clay ovens fuelled with charcoal and fed by bellows replaced the crude fire-pit. This progress culminated about 1300 in the blowing-house, a small stone building containing a granite furnace with bellows powered by a water-wheel. Layers of

*Bellows - The furnace was brought to a high temperature by a blast from the water-powered bellows.*

crushed ore and charcoal in the furnace were brought to a high temperature by the steady blast of air, liquid tin drained into a stone trough or 'float' below, and from there was ladled into stone moulds. These varied in size, but the ingots cast from them probably averaged 100-200 pounds (50-100 kilograms).

Tin of exceptional purity could now be produced by a single process, and the ceremony of the second smelting was abandoned early in the 14th century, though the metal still had to be taken to the Stannary Towns for assaying, stamping, and payment of tax. Even the smoke from the blowing-house furnace was so rich in tin that the thatch of the roof, or even the whole building, would be burned periodically to recover the trapped residue. Enlarged chimneys from which the valuable soot could be scraped were introduced in the 16th century.

As the new techniques were perfected, tin production in Devon showed a steady increase from a yearly average of around 50 tons in 1400 to a peak of 252 tons in 1524. Even this was less by a third than the output during the 12th century boom, and a gradual decline followed until the Civil War brought tinning to a temporary end. Afterwards production was sporadic until deeper mining became possible in the 18th century.

## Tin Mills

Blowing-houses were developing at the same time as improved methods of crushing ore. Crushing and smelting plants might be housed in the same building, but it is not always easy to be sure whether this was so at a particular site, where a succession of structures may have come and gone over the centuries. Traditionally all surviving tinners' buildings with a water-wheel have been called blowing-houses, though some have no trace of a furnace and were probably crushing mills only. It is now usual to be on the safe side and call them all tin mills, or tinners' mills.

Crushing and smelting mills may sometimes have belonged to particular mining concerns, but often they operated independently. Miners would bring their ore to the mills to be processed for a percentage of the product, or sell it outright. No doubt the mill-operators drove a hard bargain, but they did enable the smaller miners to work their claims without having to invest in expensive equipment.

All tin mills required a supply of water sufficient to turn an overshot wheel 8 or 10 feet in diameter. A site near a steeply-falling stream was usually chosen, so that only a short leat was needed to carry water to the top of the wheel, but a few are half a mile or more in length. Even longer leats were routinely built to supply stream and beam-works, and occasionally quite major feats of engineering were undertaken. A leat built in the 16th century to serve the tin-work at Bradford

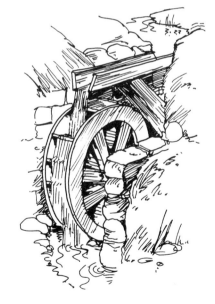

*Overshot Water-wheel - Water is carried to the top of the wheel by a wooden 'launder'.*

9

Pool, near Drewsteignton, was a full 12 miles long, and was carried across streams and valleys on aquaducts over twenty feet high.

## Charcoal

Smelting tin required huge amounts of fuel, and the tinners have sometimes been accused of destroying Dartmoor's ancient woods. In fact the high moor was treeless long before the Middle Ages, and was a 'forest' only in the sense of being a royal hunting preserve. The tinners drew their supplies of 'bushement' (faggots of brushwood) from the valleys of the border country, where their activities certainly upset local landowners, but are unlikely to have done permanent damage.

Turf and peat, on the other hand, were freely available on the moor, and successive royal charters confirmed the right of the tinners to dig for these whereever they pleased. Peat may have been used in its raw state for primative early smelting, but it could easily be converted to charcoal in the same manner as wood, by slow burning in earth mounds or granite kilns. 100 pounds of air-dried peat gave about 36 pounds of charcoal, which besides being far better fuel was lighter to transport to the smelting-site. In the 15th century charcoal from Dartmoor peat was even taken to Cornwall when fuel for smelting became scarce there. The Devon tinners do not seem to have protested, perhaps thinking the resource inexhaustible.

Peat-digging by tinners over the centuries has actually lowered the surface of the moor in places by several feet, sometimes down to bare rock. This can be seen around High Willhays (map reference SX 580895) and Okement Hill (605875), and on the ridge between Wild Tor (623877) and Quintin's Man (621839). Near Wild Tor are many remains of kilns, and hump-shaped charcoal-burners' mounds called meilers.

# FROM THE MINE
# TO THE PORTS

*Let good and legal men be appointed in the ports ... to take the oaths of all
masters and mariners that they will neither remove, nor allow to be removed,
any tin in their ships unless it be weighed and stamped by the king's customs ...*
Ordinances of William de Wrotham, 1198.

## Transport

Wheeled traffic was rare in the
Dartmoor region until the 19th
century. Pack-ponies were the
universal means of transporting
goods, and during the Middle Ages a
network of tracks and stone 'clapper'
bridges evolved to accommodate
them. Ponies carried turf, charcoal
and other supplies to the mine and
tin mills, ore to the mills if the
distance was too great for hod or
barrow, ingots of tin from the mills
to the Stannary Towns, and the
same ingots on to the ports, for
shipment to London or overseas.

*Pack-pony & Clapper Bridge*

## Coinage

Coinage was the name given to the ceremony of assaying and stamping tin
at the Stannary Towns. Until this had been done, and the proper taxes paid,
no smelted tin could legally be sold or removed from the stannary. In fact a
good deal was disposed of unofficially, either by moving the ingots to the
coasts at night, or by melting them into small bars for sale to pedlars and
sailors. Regulations made from the 12th century onwards to prevent such
practices met with little success.

Coinages normally took place in June and September, each town being dealt with in turn. Later, as increasing production made more frequent sales desirable, intermediate 'post coinages' were introduced. The town would be filled with tinners and buyers of tin, and the Controller and Receiver of the Devon stannary would arrive with the official weights and stamping-hammers in a sealed bag. These men were royal nominees, representing the interests of the Crown, while the steward of the local stannary court attended on behalf of the tinners.

At noon on the first day everyone gathered by the coinage hall, a warehouse-like building near the market-place, and the weights were solemnly unsealed. The ingots, each already stamped with its owner's mark, were brought out and weighed, then passed to the assay master, who would chisel a corner or 'coign' from the block for testing. Tin of proper quality was stamped with the royal arms or, after 1338, those of the Duchy of Cornwall. If below standard, a figure would be set at which it might be sold below the market price for pure tin. The blocks were then returned to the coinage hall until the proper tax had been paid.

Assaying may have involved matching the volume of the sample to its weight, while the consistency of the metal might be checked by rubbing against a 'touchstone' and comparing the mark with that left by a standard sample. Some tinners certainly tried to cheat the system, and vendors and smelters of 'corrupt and deceitful tin' were regularly fined or pilloried by the stannary courts.

### Destinations
Some tin was distributed overland to local markets up and down the country, but most travelled by sea. Tin from Tavistock must have been carried to Plymouth, or to Morwellham on the Tamar, and from Ashburton either to Plymouth or to Totnes and Dartmouth on the Dart. Chagford's tin went to Exeter, while Plympton was itself a port - until its estuary silted up

and trade moved downstream to Plymouth. Ironically, this was blamed on tin-mining waste washed down from the moor above.

A great deal of tin was shipped to London for the use of the pewter industry there, which dominated both the home and overseas markets. For much of the Middle Ages English pewter-ware was considered both purer and better-made than the continental product, and even after the Flemish and German industries began to catch up in the 16th century we are told that foreigners still preferred 'garnishes of good flat English pewter'.

Most raw tin was also exported from London, especially to Flanders and northern France, but some went directly from Devon ports to southern Europe. Bourdeaux was a main distribution centre for English tin in the early Middle Ages. In the 14th century it was displaced by Bruges, but by then direct sea-routes had been opened up between England and the Mediterranean, and Italian traders were attending the Devon coinages. Smugglers meanwhile maintained a steady traffic from Devon to Holland, or more discreetly by way of the Channel Islands.

13

# THE TINNERS

*Some beeings dealers for tynne ... when occasion of trouble cometh only uppon Tynners ... then they say that they are noe Tynners. On the other parte the same men goinge about to receive their debts ... then confesse they them selves to bee Tynners, and will not sticke to pleade the same in Courte.*

The Baliff of Blackmore, 1586.

**Who were the tinners?**

Almost anyone connected with the tin industry could claim to be a tinner, entitled to stannary privileges and the protection of the stannary courts. Dealers in tin, suppliers of goods and services to the industry, and anyone with the slightest financial interest in tinning, all called themselves tinners when it suited them. The real tinners, though, were the miners and mill-workers, who in an account book of 1586 were divided into the following categories.

> Master Tinners owned shares in tin-works, but took no part in the labour, either employing workers or leasing out their rights.
>
> The ordinary Tinner might own a share in a mine and work it himself, or rent a share, for which he paid about 20% of the tin produced. Another class of workers took a share in the venture for a fixed period, keeping only half their tin but receiving a yearly wage of around 45 shillings (£2.25) which they could live on between sales.
>
> Dole-workers took a part-share in the mine for their own benefit, but had to work another part-share for which they received only a small wage, about one pound a year.
>
> Labourers were employed by the year for a fixed wage, not exceeding £4.10.0 (£4.50). They took no part in the profits of their work.

Spalliards were casual labourers taken on during the wash, or whenever extra workers were needed, for a wage of about 4d a day (1½p). The term spalliard comes from an old English verb meaning to chip or split, and signifies a breaker of stones. Spadiard, or spade-worker, was another name for such men.

Not every mining venture involved all these different classes of people. Under the laws of the stannaries, anyone could work for tin wherever he chose, simply by laying out a claim with piles of stones or turf marking the corners, and registering these 'bounds' with the stannary court. A single man, working part-time with shovel and bucket for a few loads of stream-ore, was as much a tinner as the partner in a large syndicate employing many labourers and the latest equipment.

There were few fortunes to be made by the small independent miner. For him, as for the paid labourer, tinning often provided no more than a seasonal addition to income from other occupations. Tinners might be smallholders or tradesmen, or engage in some craft ancillary to tinning, like charcoal-burning; or they might alternate between working their own bounds and taking pay as spalliards in some larger operation.

Freedom of choice was the great benefit conferred on the working tinner by stannary law. Even the poorest serf could become his own master by staking a claim, and such privilege was rare in the Middle Ages; but the work was back-breaking, sometimes dangerous, and at best involved living out on the moor in crude shelters, for days or weeks at a time in all weathers. The well-known description of a 17th century miner's life in Thomas Westcote's *A view of Devonshire* cannot be bettered.

*No labourer whatsoever undergoes greater hazard of peril or danger, nor in hard or coarse fare and diet doth equal him: bread, the brownest; cheese, the hardest; drink, the thinnest; yea, commonly the dew of heaven, which he taketh from his shovel, or spade, or in the hollow of his hand ... He spends all day (or the major part thereof) like a mole or earthworm underground, mining in deep vaults or pits, as though he intended (with noble Sir Francis Drake) to find a way to the antipodes; yea, a nearer, and so to surpass him: for it is somewhat of that profundity, that notwithstanding the country (so they term the earth over their heads) is propped, posted, crossed, traversed, and supported with divers great beams of timber to keep them in security, yet all is sometimes too little; they perish with the fall thereof notwithstanding.*

## Who were the owners?

Records of the 12th and 13th centuries show that Jews were closely concerned with early mining in Devon, though whether as traders in tin, financiers of mining ventures, or as miners themselves is not clear. Edward I expelled all the Jews from England in 1291, and this has sometimes been blamed for a temporary fall in tin production that occured during the next ten years. As late as the 19th century, remains of medieval tinners' buildings on Dartmoor were commonly called Jews' Houses.

In the later Middle Ages, it becomes clear that ownership of shares in tin-works was spread across a wide spectrum of society. The lists of people paying coinage duty include yeomen, tradesmen, some women, and a number of prosperous landowners and minor gentry. Examples of the last class were branches of the Knapman and Endacott families of Throwleigh, and the Whiddons of Chagford, who owned mines and blowing-mills in the Okehampton area during the 16th and 17th centuries.

Also prominent were the religious guilds attached to many Devon parish churches. The accounts of the Chagford churchwardens, which survive from 1480, show that the Guilds of St Michael, St Katherine, St Mary and several others were all deeply involved in mining ventures. This may explain the tradition that many Devon churches were rebuilt in the 15th century with wealth derived from tin.

Large landowners did invest in the tin industry, but it never fell under their control, and the occasional nobleman in the coinage list rubs shoulders with bakers and tanners. In 1494 the Stannary Parliament made a deliberate effort to preserve this state of affairs by forbidding owners of land above the yearly value of ten pounds to acquire any new interest in tinworks. Plainly the tinners of Dartmoor set a high value on independence, and to a great extent they managed to maintain it.

**Holiday pastimes**
The labouring classes of Devon, tinners included, played as hard as they worked. *'Their holy-days' exercises were toilsome and violent,'* says Thomas Westcote, *'as wrestling, hurling, football, leaping, running, dancing with music, especially in their festivals, to exhilarate their hearts and such like; which made them fit for the wars, or any other employment whatsoever, wherein hardiness, or strength, or agility was required.'* The puritan zeal of the early 17th century frowned on such recreations and tried to suppress them; but Westcote hints that the attempt was unlikely to be successful, for the Devonians were *'liberi homines - free men of state and condition: no slaves,'* and not even puritanism could curb their spirits for long.

The tin mill at Upper Merrivale, on the west bank of the River Walkham (SX 5519 7665) was excavated by the Dartmoor Tinworking Research Group in 1991-94. Both smelting and stamping took place here at various times, with power supplied by two water-wheels. On the left of the photograph is a mould stone, used for casting tin ingots.

An alternative view of the Upper Merrivale tin mill. The furnace was immediately to the left of the mould stone.

*A mould stone and mortar stones at Upper Merrivale. The water-powered stamps used for crushing tin ore worked up and down on the mortar stones, creating the circular depressions.*

*The lower of two tin mills on the east bank of the Walkham at Merrivale (SX 5527 7535). A mould stone can be seen just inside the doorway, with the mouth of the furnace to the right.*

19

# THE ECONOMICS OF TIN

*Receipts: 10s 11d [55p] for black tin sold to John Newcombe of Ayreston. 16d [7p] for income received from a certain tin-work lying near Chagford Bridge. Paid to John Splott for labour in a certain tin-work called Seynt Katherine's Beme in this year, 5s 6d [27¹/₂p] . And paid to John Man for labour in a certain tin-work called Cherebroke 2s 6d [12¹/₂p].*
*Paid for beer bought when receiving the profits on the tin-work called Chagford Brigge, 1d ... For a shovel for tin-mining 11d [4¹/₂p].*

Accounts of the wardens of St Michael's Church,
Chagford, 1526.

### Prices and wages

In the early Middle Ages, prices and wages tended to rise very gradually together. At the end of the 13th century an unskilled labourer was paid about a penny a day, while a skilled artisan might earn up to 4d. The labour supply was drastically reduced in the mid-14th century by the plague known as the Black Death, and wages soon doubled while prices remained static. The paid labourer of 1500 was relatively well-off with 2d a day.

Towards the middle of the 16th century rapid inflation set in. By the end of the century wages had doubled again, but the cost of living was six times higher, and people living only on wages suffered accordingly. This was true of tinners as much as anyone, but many had other occupations to fall back on, and a spalliard who was also a tradesman or smallholder was compensated by the higher prices he could get for his produce.

Labourers in the tin industry were slightly better paid than agricultural workers, but they put up with harsher conditions. The farmhand, as Thomas Westcote remarked in 1630, *'labours without danger and much more easily, (and) dieth after a better sort.'*

## The price of tin

Tin prices varied from year to year, but a pound of tin was worth about 1d in 1200. As the use of the metal increased so did its value, and by 1500 the average price was 4d (1¹/₂p) a pound. Prices in general had not risen much during those centuries, so tin was a good investment. The inflation of the 16th century changed matters, with tin prices varying erratically but falling in real terms, so that mining ventures became less attractive, and the industry began to decline.

## How much tin was produced?

Production of tin was affected by many things besides prices, such as the availability of ore and the methods used to mine and smelt it. During the peak period 1171-89, when stream-ore was plentiful, the yearly average was about 343 tons (349 tonnes). By the last decade of the 13th century it had fallen to only 33 tons, and slow improvement was interrupted by the Black Death, which upset the industry so badly that in 1355 no tin at all was coined in Devon. Production did not recover until the 1370s, but after that a steady increase was maintained as new mining and dressing techniques were perfected.

Figures for average annual production over the next 250 years can easily be extracted from the coinage lists; but it must not be forgotten that they underestimate the amount of metal actually produced. The Dartmoor tinners were adept at the unofficial disposal of their product, and ingots that had never known the coinage hammer were hurried aboard ship by night, or melted into small bars suited to concealment in a pedlar's pack or sailor's kit-bag.

| Years | Tons | Average tons per year |
|-------|------|----------------------|
| 1400-1450 | 2704 | 54 |
| 1450-1500 | 5196 | 104 |
| 1500-1550 | 9944 | 199 |
| 1550-1600 | 4655 | 93 |
| 1600-1650 | 1250 | 25 |

## A time of prosperity

The late 15th and early 16th centuries were prosperous times in Devon, and their legacy is still to be seen in the substantial new houses erected for yeomen and gentry, and in hundreds of churches rebuilt in the self-assured Perpendicular style. For this the wool trade was largely responsible, but wealth from tin played its part, and later generations of tinners looked back on a golden age of the industry, when production and profits were high, and workmen earned good wages. The year 1524, when 252 tons of tin were coined, marks a peak that would never be attained again.

## Taxation

In 1198 the newly-appointed Warden of the Stannaries, William de Wrotham, reported that ' by ancient custom' the king received 2s 6d (12½p) for every thousandweight of tin (1200 pounds = 550 kilograms), after its first smelting. This amounted to less than 3% of the metal's current market value, and a new tax was promptly imposed of 13s 4d (67p) on every thousandweight at the second smelting. The old customary payment had brought the Crown only £80 in 1191, whereas the two taxes produced £600 in 1199. Comparisons with modern money are difficult but, on the basis that a labourer of the late 12th century might earn a penny a day, the new income was equivalent to several million pounds. The duty on the first smelting increased during the 13th century to 4s 8d (23p), and some further small charges were introduced. Between 1243 and 1301 the so-called black rent of 2d a year was imposed on every digger of tin-ore, and in 1288 came the white rent, collected from owners of smelted 'white' tin. At first this was paid in kind, at a rate of two pounds of tin per head, but after 1400 it became a fixed charge of 8d.

Improved technology put an end to the separate taxes on the first and second smeltings, and both were replaced in 1302 by a new 'coinage' duty of 1s 6¾d on every hundredweight of tin (equivalent to 120 pounds, not

112, in tin-weighing terms). Production was now far lower than it had been a century before, and in 1303 the new tax raised only £69 17s 1d (£69.85p), rising to £368 9s 1d in the peak year of 1524.

The Crown's other financial benefits from the tin industry included toll for tin mines on royal manors, fees for export licences, and customs dues on exported tin. There was also a right to 'pre-empt' or compulsorily purchase tin, which was then re-sold. This brought a profit of £352 6s 10d in 1197. The right of pre-emption was often leased to the warden, or to groups of merchants.

**Tax exemption**
The tinners did have some compensation for all these impositions. They were exempt not only from local tolls and market dues, but from ordinary national taxation. The Crown sometimes had second thoughts about this, and in 1338 an attempt was made to collect the taxes known as the 'tenth and fifteenth' from tinners. A concerted strike in the stannaries resulted, and the idea was hastily dropped.

# LAWS AND PRIVILEGES
# OF THE STANNARIES

*The stannary men commit trespass and assault ... nor permit themselves to be brought to justice according to the law and custom of the realm, and when the hue and cry is raised against them, they take and beat the King's bailiffs and ... imprison them in the stannary gaol until a ransom is paid.*

Complaint of certain men of Devon,
Patent Rolls 12 Edward II (1318).

### Ancient rights and customs

When the mining laws of Devon were first recorded at the beginning of the 13th century, tinners were already privileged 'by ancient custom' to dig for tin wherever they chose, to divert streams, and to take wood and turf for fuel. Owners of land had no prior claim to minerals, and could not hinder the miner's activities, though they were entitled to a toll of one fifteenth of his produce. The origin of these customs is unknown, but they may have evolved in the older Cornish industry, and been adopted by the tinners of Devon when mining began there.

The Norman kings of England soon saw the value of controlling the tin industry, and by the 12th century the old customary laws had been embodied in a set of regulations called the Assize of Mines. At this time the whole of Devon was classed as a royal forest, subject to special laws for preserving game, and the officials and courts of the forest were conveniently on hand to enforce mining law. In 1195 Lydford Castle was built as

*Lydford Castle*

24

a prison for offenders against both codes, and the grim keep remained for centuries the symbol of a harsh and summary justice.

Among the matters regulated by the Assize of Mines was the system of bounding, or staking claims by marking the corners of an area with piles of stone or turf. Records from these early times are sparse, but the courts must have ensured that bounds were not infringed, and that claimants had actually begun to produce ore within a reasonable period. Smelting was also regulated, to ensure that ingots were duly stamped and the proper tax paid. Taxes were collected by the sheriff of the county, who usually 'farmed' them; that is, he agreed to pay a lump sum to the Crown and made a profit from whatever tax-money he could extract in excess of that amount.

## Royal officials and charters

At the end of the 12th century a royal official called the Warden of the Stannaries was appointed to exercise direct supervision over the tin industry. William de Wrotham, the second warden whose name is recorded, assumed office in 1198 with instructions to increase the king's revenue, which he did by imposing a heavy new duty on the second smelting of tin, and issuing ordinances to regulate tax-collection and prevent smuggling. From now on, the warden replaced both the sheriff and the forest courts in the financial and legal business of the stannaries.

In 1201 King John codified the new state of affairs. *'We have granted that the Chief Warden of the Stannaries ... have over the tinners plenary power to do them justice and ... to receive them in our prisons, if it shall happen that any of [them] ought to be seized ... for the tinners are of our farm and always in our demesene.'*

This was an important concession. Dartmoor was a royal property whose inhabitants had always claimed special rights as the king's tenants, but now

25

tinners everywhere had that status. Any serf could become the king's man simply by finding work as a tinner, and no ordinary court could compel him to return to his former lord. *'They shall not be called from their work by any summons except that of the Chief Warden'*, the charter promised, and the tinners guarded that privilege jealously down the centuries, often to the envy and resentment of their neighbours.

Devon ceased to be royal forest in 1204, except for Dartmoor and Exmoor. In 1239 Henry III gave Dartmoor Forest and the stannaries to his brother Richard, Earl of Cornwall, and the warden was appointed by the earls until 1300, when the crown resumed control. In 1305 Edward 1 issued a new charter which largeley confirmed the old, except that only tinners working on the royal demesne were declared immune from being claimed as serfs. The status of those working elsewhere remained open to dispute - especially when Dartmoor was given in 1337 to the newly-created Duchy of Cornwall, and so ceased to be the king's own land.

The 1305 charter also exempted tinners from local and national taxes. Chagford, Tavistock and Ashburton were established as Stannary Towns for the colection of coinage duty, and Lydford Castle as the stannary prison. Although tinners could be tried by the ordinary courts for serious offences concerning 'land, life or limb', they could not be kept in custody anywhere but at Lydford. For most purposes they had become an independent community, separate both from the ordinary systems of local government and law-enforcement, and from the rest of rural society under its manorial lords.

### Complaints
Inevitably there were complaints that the tinners abused their special position. In 1314 the 'poor men of the county of Devon' claimed that farm land, wood and meadow, and even houses and gardens, were being destroyed at the rate of 300 acres a year. In 1318 we hear of tinners refusing to pay

the toll due to landowners, but instead extorting money from those whose property they invaded. When challenged they resisted arrest, or used violence to prevent people attending the local courts, and tinners supposed to be in custody at Lydford for felony were being allowed to run loose. Ten petitions were presented to Parliament in 1320 alone, and others in 1347 and 1376. Governments would sometimes make a show of investigating abuses, but the king had an eye to his revenue, and could be relied on to uphold the tinners against every attack.

**The stannary courts**
William de Wrotham's first court in 1198 was convened at Exeter, and the wardens probably continued to hold court wherever it was most convenient. Later the chief court of the Devon stannaries, usually presided over by the vice-warden, seems to have settled at Lydford. District courts are heard of as early as 1243, and after 1305 were located in the Stannary Towns of Chagford, Ashburton and Tavistock. When Plympton joined the group in 1328, Devon was divided into four territories or stannaries, whose boundaries met at the centre of Dartmoor, near Crockern Tor.

*The Four Stannary Districts*

Cases in the district courts were decided by a jury of tinners, under the presidency of a steward appointed by the warden. Thirteen sessions were held annually, of which two in the spring and autumn were called law courts and were supposed to be attended by every tinner in the district. As well as trying civil and criminal cases, they dealt with administrative matters such as registering bounds, verifying weights and measures, and ensuring that bailiffs and other officials were doing their jobs efficiently.

The established local courts did not welcome the competition of the stannary jurisdiction. Justice in the Middle Ages was expected to make a profit, and the landowners and officials of the county found not only their authority impaired, but their income reduced. A particular grievance was that the stannary courts did not confine themselves to matters directly concerned with tin-mining, but heard cases of every kind where a tinner was involved, while anyone who sued a tinner in another court would have to answer for it. Even the powerful officials of the forest were liable to be fined for interfering with those whom the tin-courts took under their protection.

Litigants wanting a quick result were naturally eager to make use of courts whose proceedings were brief and informal, and whose verdicts were backed by the threat of the Lydford dungeons. Critics complained that the term 'tinner' should include only working miners, whereas the stannary jurors stretched it to cover sharholders in mines and mills, dealers in tin, and every tradesman and artisan supplying the industry. The argument was never formally settled, but in practice the stannary courts heard whatever cases they chose and paid no attention to contrary opinions.

### The case of Richard Strode M.P.

The refusal of the stannary courts to recognise any jurisdiction but their own is exemplified in the famous case of Richard Strode, a wealthy owner of tin works who was Member of Parliament for Plympton in 1512. In the hope of evicting unwelcome tinners from his own land, he introduced a bill at Westminster to restrain mining operations near the Devon ports, which he alleged were in danger of being choked by mine refuse. The bill did not become law, but aroused great indignation among the tinners, and Strode was fined £40 in each of the four district courts. On his refusal to pay, he was arrested and *'imprysoned in a dongeon and a deepe pitte under the ground in the castel of Lidford'*, where he languished for three weeks before obtaining his release.

To secure himself against further persecution, Strode persuaded the Westminster parliament to pass a statute annulling his condemnation and granting him immunity for anything done by him in that or future parliaments. This early assertion of the parliamentary privilege of free speech gained Strode his place in constitutional history, and marks a stage in the suppression by central government of competing local jurisdictions. The stannary courts in 1512 had reached a peak of power and arrogance, from which they would now swiftly decline.

## The Tinners' Parliament

According to tradition, the tinners of Devon and Cornwall in the early Middle Ages used to meet in general assembly every seven or eight years at Hingston Down, near Callington in Cornwall. Later the Devon tinners held their own assembly at Crockern Tor near Two Bridges, where the boundaries of the four stannaries converged. It was called the Great Court, or parliament, and its object was *'to consult, enquire, and take deliberation ... for the redressing and amending of any inconveniences or abuses within the Stannaries'*. Records of its meetings survive only from 1494, but it may have existed for centuries before that.

The Great Court was held at no set times, but convened by the warden or vice-warden when he thought fit. All tinners were summoned to attend the next sitting of their local stannary court, where they would elect 24 jurates or stannators to represent them, a uniquely democratic system for its time which has prompted comparison with the national parliament in London. The names of the jurates of 1494 and some later meetings are known, and many are those of families still resident in the same districts today.

On the appointed day, the 96 stannators assembled in the presence of the vice-warden at Crockern Tor. Here they made and amended the laws of the stannaries, and re-affirmed their ancient rights. A statute of 1494 forbade clergy, stannary officials, and owners of land above the yearly value of £10 to acquire any new interest in tinworks, while another debarred professional lawyers from pleading in any tin-court. More conventional decrees dealt with registration of bounds, and stamping of smelters' marks on ingots. In 1510 a penalty of £40 was fixed for contravening the right of tinners to dig where they chose, and it was for infringing this statute that Richard Strode was condemned.

Six meetings of the parliament in the 16th century are recorded, the last in 1574. After that they grew infrequent, and ceased altogether in the 18th century. A meeting is said to have been held as late as 1749, but by then it was the custom merely to open the court at Crockern Tor, before adjourning to the pleasanter surroundings of Tavistock. The stone chairs and table of the stannators have long vanished, but the so-called Judge's Seat still exists, two miles away at Dunnabridge pound.

# THE FOUR STANNARY TOWNS

*We Will and straightly command that all Tyn as well white as black wheresoever it shal be bestowed ... be wayghed at Tavistock, Asperton & Chaggeforde by our wayghts thereto ordayned. We have granted also for us & our heires that all our tynners aforesaid all this tyn so wayed lawfully may sel to whom they will in the townes aforesaid ... Except we or our heires will buy the said tyn ourselves.*

*A true Copie of the Charter or grant
made by King Edward the First, 1305.*

The expansion of the Dartmoor tin industry in the Middle Ages made a profound impact on the four towns which served as distribution centres for the smelted metal. Chagford, Tavistock, Plympton and Ashburton had all been market towns where tin was smelted and sold as early as the 12th century. After 1305, as designated Stannary Towns, their fortunes were even more intimately linked with that of the industry. Stannary status brought commercial and political gains, but automatic prosperity was by no means assured.

## Ashburton

Ashburton governed the south-east quarter of Dartmoor, an area stretching from Widecombe to Ugborough. The town lay midway between Exeter and Plympton, and was a regional centre for tin distribution at least from the late 12th century. Early in the 14th century it was chief among the Stannary Towns, and more than half of all the tin produced in Devon was coined there. Later the coinages declined until in 1595 they represented only one fifth of the total.

The tin industry was prone to fluctuations, and even a Stannary Town needed other trades to achieve lasting stability. Like Chagford and

Tavistock, Ashburton became an important centre for woollen cloth, and also for corn and cattle. The town obtained a charter for a Saturday market in 1310, and had two annual fairs at the festivals of St Martin and St Lawrence; but in 1349 came the Black Death, which returned in repeated waves during the second half of the century. In 1377 the population was less than half what it had been in 1300.

Ashburton seems to have stayed in decline through the 15th and most of the 16th centuries, despite the success of the tin industry during those years. In the 1580s it recovered some of its old stature as a cloth town, specialising in the light worsted fabrics which were then coming into fashion. Prosperity lasted into the 19th century, but after 1833 the wool trade collapsed. By-passed by the railways, Ashburton sank to being a minor country market town, and the old house in East Street where the stannary court had sat was pulled down.

**Chagford**

The Stannary of Chagford comprised the north-east quarter of Dartmoor, from Okehampton to Widecombe. Like Ashburton, Chagford became an important centre for Dartmoor wool as well as tin, but with the decline of both these industries in modern times the town came to derive most of its trade from tourism. The Churchwardens' accounts, which survive for the years 1480 - 1600, show that the church guilds were heavily involved in the tin industry, owning shares in tin-works over a wide area between Okehampton and Moretonhampstead.

A dramatic event in the town's history was the sudden collapse of the Stannary Court House on 7th March 1617. The contemporary account of the disaster is written as a homily against falsehood and swearing. The court was in session, with many 'good and worshipful gentlemen' present, when an obviously false accusation was brought forward under oath. The judges admonished the 'audacious fellow', who unwisely replied: *"If I sweare amisse ... let God I beseech him make me a fearful example to all perjured wretches and that this house wherein I stand may sodainely fall upon my head."*

No sooner had the 'cursed imprecation' been spoken than the roof and walls of the house, though they seemed strong and the weather was fine, did indeed suddenly fall down! The false accuser and several others, including the steward of the court, were struck dead, and seventeen were badly injured, 'their limbs almost beaten in pieces'. The shocking event 'not only amazed the whole town but strooke a trembling fear throughout all the neighbouring villages'. Miraculously, a young child was found unhurt among the heap of timber, stone and earth, 'preserved in the midst of these men of more able strength, which lay as it were with their brains dashed out.'

## Tavistock

Tavistock controlled the area from Plymouth to Okehampton, west of the rivers Meavy and West Dart. Early in the reign of Henry I the town was granted a weekly market and a three-day fair at the feast of St Rumon (29-31 August), which soon attracted merchants coming to buy tin. A thriving trade in woollen cloth also grew up, and this saved the town from ruin when the tin industry declined. In the 18th century the wool trade in turn fell into decay, but then came new prosperity with the opening of rich copper mines in the district, which proved a steady source of wealth until finally exhausted in the early 20th century.

The rise of the medieval town was encouraged by the abbots of Tavistock Abbey, who saw the hamlet outside their gates become a thriving urban community during the first great expansion of the tin trade. Abbot Robert Champeaux was appointed Warden of the Stannaries in 1319; but in 1324 a quarrel over the succession to the abbacy brought a disastrous three-year vacancy, which wrecked the abbey's prosperity, and left Tavistock without firm leadership at a time when the merchants of Plympton were plotting to usurp its status as a Stannary Town.

## Plympton

The Stannary of Plympton covered the south-west quarter of the moor, between the rivers Erme and Meavy. Plympton was the last of the four towns to gain stannary status, and the attempt to do so at the expense of its rival, Tavistock, shows how fiercely that privilege and its attendant profits were coveted.

In 1327 a group of Plympton townsmen presented a petition to the Crown, in the name of all the tinners of Devon, asking for the coinage of tin to be removed from Tavistock to Plympton. They argued that Plympton was a port where tin could be transferred directly to ships, while Tavistock was so far inland that few traders went there to buy tin because of the high transport costs. In fact Tavistock had its own port on the Tamar, and was far nearer the sea than Chagford; but the government ordered the sheriff of Devon, Roger Rodde, to hold an enquiry.

For whatever reason, the sheriff's jury turned out to consist entirely of men from Plympton and its neighbourhood, whose verdict was predictable. In 1328 the coinage was duly transferred; but protests followed from the Dartmoor tinners (especially those of Tavistock), drawing attention to the packed jury and pointing out that the enquiry should anyway have been held by the Warden of the Stannaries, not the sheriff. A compromise was presently reached, with Tavistock reinstated while Plympton kept its new dignity. The Devon stannary was now divided into four quarters, with the boundaries meeting near Crockern Tor at the centre of Dartmoor. This story has an ironic footnote. The workings of the tinners upstream were later blamed for the silting-up of the Plym estuary; so the very industry in which Plympton was eager to involve itself may have caused the town's demise as a port, and the loss of its trade to Plymouth.

# LEGENDS AND TRADITIONS OF THE STANNARIES

*They have a castle on a hill,*
*I took it for an old windmill,*
*The vanes blown off by weather ...*
*Ten men less room within this cave*
*Than five mice in a lantern have.*
*I know none gladly there would stay,*
*But rather hang out of the way.*

William Browne, 1644.

The medieval tinners themselves have gained an almost legendary status reflected in the popular description of them as the 'old men' of the moor. We can only guess what they thought about the harsh environment in which they worked, but they are not likely to have been less superstitious than their successors, the later miners, who continued to trust in charms and rituals for protection against the dangers of their trade, holding it unlucky to work on Midsummer Eve, New Year's Eve and New Year's Day, and mounting horse-shoes around their buildings to ward off witchcraft. A deep respect for the moor itself is evident in some of the legends that have come down to modern times.

## Old Crockern

The strange forms of the Dartmoor tors have always been a source of fascination to those who worked in their shadow, and some have had magical qualities ascribed to them. Most important to the tinners was Crockern Tor, seat of the Stannary Parliament. It was a convenient meeting-place, where the boundaries of the four stannaries converged; but traditions associating the tor with far older ceremonial gatherings may have played a part in drawing the tinners to this inhospitable spot.

Reverence for some force inherent in the bleak landscape runs through the story of 'Old Crockern', who is said to haunt the tor. A ghostly grey figure astride a skeleton horse, he ranges across the moor at midnight, wielding a threatening sword.

Tradition tells of a rich Manchester farmer who visited Dartmoor and decided the land was ripe for cultivation. He set about enclosing the land about Crockern Tor, but soon made himself unpopular with his grasping ways. One day a simpleton warned him of a dream in which the spirit of the moor, 'Old Crockern isself', had expressed disapproval of the farmer's plans and vowed, *"If he scratches my back I'll tear his pocket out."* The Manchester man scoffed at the tale, but the prophecy was fulfilled. After many years of scratching the moor's obdurate surface, he gave up and returned home with his pockets empty. Old Crockern had proved true to his word.

*'Old Crockern isself'*

## The legend of Chaw Gully Mine

Many dartmoor tin-lodes contain small amounts of gold, and it is said that the finest tin and largest amounts of gold lie hidden in the depths of Chaw Gully Mine, on the slope of Challacombe Down. However, legend also has it that the treasure is protected by demons that lurk in the subterranean galleries of the old mine. On a high crag above perches a fierce old raven, said to be the very one dispatched from the ark by Noah. When foolhardy miners descend the shaft on ropes, the raven utters a warning croak, and those watching above see a hand holding a knife emerge fom the side of the shaft, to sever the explorers' lifeline and send them plunging to their deaths. The next morning their corpses will be found on the surface, since the evil spirits below cannot rest with the body of a Christian among them.

## Lydford Law

The medieval Stannary Courts have left behind their own tradition of harsh and terrible punishments. Reputedly, the penalty in olden days for selling impure tin was to have a quantity of it melted and poured down one's throat! More probably such a crime resulted in a fine or a spell in the stocks or pillory, perhaps preceded by an unpleasant visit to Lydford Castle, built in the 12th century as a prison for offenders against the strict forest and stannary laws.

Early in the 16th century Lydford Castle was described as 'one of the most annoious, contagious and detestable places wythin this realme'. In 1644 William Browne, the Tavistock poet, wrote:

> *I oft have heard of Lydford Law*
> *How in the morn they hang and draw*
> *And sit in judgement after ...*

which one hopes was an exaggeration. The legend used by Browne may however preserve a tradition of proceedings in the early Forest Courts, which sat so seldom that sentences might actually be carried out before they were formally confirmed.

The castle's bloody reputation later let it to be associated with Lord Chief Justice Jeffreys (1648-89), the notorious 'hanging judge' whose Bloody Assizes after the Monmouth rebellion of 1685 made him a popular bogey throughout the West Country. He had no connection with the stannaries, and is unlikely ever to have presided at Lydford; but legend is stonger than fact, and the old judge is said to haunt the castle mound in the shape of a black pig.

### The Tinners' Rabbits?

On roof-bosses in a number of Devon churches are depicted three rabbits, sharing three ears between them. This device is generally known as The Tinners' Rabbits, and is often claimed to have been the emblem of the medieval tinners. It is found in several parishes which were important tin-working centres, notably Chagford, Tavistock and Widecombe, and this is cited as evidence that other churches where it appears were built or restored by the tinners. To clinch the matter, we learn that Dartmoor's medieval rabbit-warrens were also created by the tinners, who took the burrowing rabbit for their badge in allusion to their own underground life-style; and that the alchemists of the Middle Ages used the symbol to represent the element tin.

*The Tinners' Rabbits'*

None of these suppositions is supported by much evidence. Wealth from the tin industry certainly played its part in rebuilding many Devon churches, but most are without rabbits. Only seven Dartmoor parishes have them, whereas they appear at Iddesleigh, Sampford Courtenay, Spreyton and Bridford, which have no strong tin-mining associations. The link with alchemy seems to be spurious, and though the tinners may indeed have built rabbit buries on Holne Moor and elsewhere, this alone would give them no title to the symbol. There is no written evidence to connect them with it before the mid-19th century.

It is even debatable whether the creatures are rabbits at all. They may be meant for hares, which have been seen as sacred or magical beasts in many cultures. The Roman goddess of love was represented in astrology by a three-hare symbol known as the 'Hunt of Venus', and this may have been redefined for Christian purposes as a figure of the Holy Trinity. Pagan symbols of that kind, Green Men and the like, are common enough in Devon churches to account for the rabbits without dragging in the tinners at all. Still, some connection cannot be ruled out, and might account for rabbits (or hares) being chosen to symbolize the Trinity in Devon in preference to the more usual fishes.

### The death-call of Crazywell Pool

Crazywell Pool, south of Raddick Hill near Princetown, owes its present appearance to the excavations of tinners, though it may originally have been a natural pond. In Tudor times it was used as a reserviour to supply nearby tin-works. Various superstitions surround the lonely hollow, with its steep sides and acre-wide expanse of dark water. We are told that the bell-ropes of Walkhampton Church were once tied together, but could not touch the bottom. The pool is indeed said to be bottomless, and to communicate in some mysterious way with the sea, since it rises and falls with the Plymouth tides!

Moorland workers made long detours to avoid the spot, especially at dawn and dusk, when a ghostly voice calls out the name of anyone whose death is imminent. At midnight on Midsummer Eve the face of the next person due to die in Walkhampton parish can be seen reflected in the still water.

A modern addition to the pool's legend reports how two local youths were challanged to go there on Midsummer Eve. They saw only their own reflections, and laughed at the old tales; but as they rode home that night their motor-bike failed to negotiate a bend on the Roborough road, and both were killed.

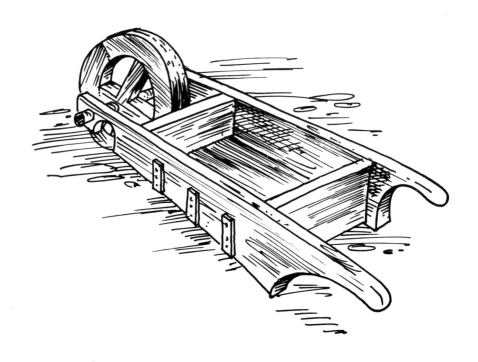